THE FOSSIL GROVE

ALASTAIR GUNNING

Glasgow Museums

Director's Preface

I welcome the publication of this new book on the Fossil Grove. It is part of our plan to develop the potential of this remarkable site, one of the newer additions to Glasgow Museums.

In keeping with the foresight of those who ensured the preservation of the Fossil Grove following its discovery over 100 years ago this book continues our commitment to upgrade the facilities and improve the interpretation of the site. This will enhance its appeal and value for visitors.

Thanks are due to the following for their help in the preparation of this book; Hunterian Museum University of Glasgow; Lavinia Drew, Scaramouche Promotions; Alan McKirdy, Scottish Natural Heritage; Jimmie Murray, Glasgow School of Art and T Norman Tait, Department of Botany, University of Glasgow. I am also grateful to all staff of Glasgow Museums who assisted with its production.

The recent developments at Fossil Grove have been facilitated by financial contributions from Britoil plc, the European Regional Development Fund, Scotseal Ltd and Svenska Handelsbanken and I would like to take this opportunity to express our thanks to them. Much of this assistance has been made available through the efforts of the members of the Fossil Grove Trust.

Julian Spalding
Director, Glasgow Museums

Introduction

Fossil Grove must be Glasgow's oldest attraction. The spectacular fossil trees which can be seen at this famous site are relics of a distant past–a past when the area was a very different place from today. The city is fortunate to possess such an outstanding geological monument.

It is situated within Glasgow's Victoria Park, in the Whiteinch area of the city, near the north entrance to the Clyde Tunnel. The building which protects the site can be found towards the south-west corner of the park in a tranquil setting surrounded by the enclosing walls of a beautifully landscaped old quarry. Inside the fossil house the underlying rock strata are laid bare over an area of about 23 metres by 10 metres. The scene is dominated by a group of large tree stumps in the centre of the excavated area. These are fossil trees now composed of stone, not wood. In total 11 fossil tree stumps were uncovered by the excavations. These preserved remains represent a natural group of trees still in the position in which they were once growing. What has been fossilised is only a small corner of a vast tropical forest, now long disappeared, which at one time thrived in the area.

Fossil Grove is not the only site where this kind of fossil tree has been found. Isolated stumps or small groups have been recorded at many other places in rocks of the same age. Other examples exist from the Glasgow area. For instance a small group of trees was uncovered in 1868 at Gilmorehill in a quarry being worked for sandstone used in the building of Glasgow University. Unfortunately the fossils here were destroyed by further quarrying activity. The Grove is by far the most impressive group uncovered and the only one which has been carefully excavated with the trees preserved on site so that they can still be viewed in association with each other and with the surrounding rock strata. The significance of Fossil Grove has been recognised through its designation as a Site of Special Scientific Interest by Scottish Natural Heritage.

As well as being a monument to a past geological age Fossil Grove is also an apt reminder of a vital aspect of Glasgow's development in the more recent past. It preserves the remains of the same forests which gave rise to the many coal seams present in the rocks underlying the city. Each coal seam was formed by the compaction and hardening of thick layers of plant debris which built up on the floors of these forests. No mining industry survives today but the coals were once extensively worked in local pits and easy access to abundant reserves of fuel provided a stimulus to Glasgow's growth into a large and important industrial city.

Fossil Grove building situated in a picturesque corner of Victoria Park

General view of Fossil Grove interior showing four of the tree stumps

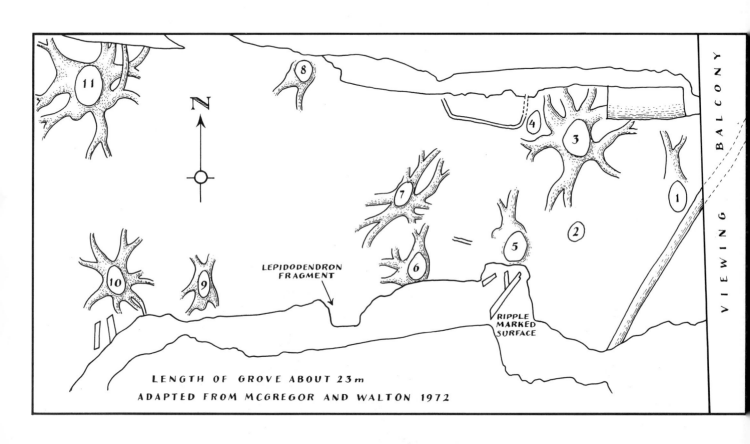

VIEWING BALCONY

11

8

4

3

1

7

2

5

6

LEPIDODENDRON
FRAGMENT

10

9

RIPPLE
MARKED
SURFACE

N

LENGTH OF GROVE ABOUT 23m
ADAPTED FROM MCGREGOR AND WALTON 1972

Plan of Fossil Grove
Trees numbered 1 to 11

Discovery

View of newly completed excavations prior to erection of the building

Fossil Grove was discovered in 1887. Land had just been obtained by the local authorities with a view to creating a public park in the area. Local unemployment was high at this time due to a depression in the shipbuilding industry and the scheme was seen as a way of providing some work. Laying-out started in 1886 and Victoria Park, named in honour of the Queen's Jubilee, was officially opened to the public on 5 July 1887. Discovery of the fossils was made slightly later that year when a small, disused quarry within the park boundaries was being landscaped. The rock walls of this quarry still surround the Grove today. It had been excavated in a small hill known as Quarry Knowe to work a layer of dolerite or whinstone, used locally for roadmaking and as part of the landscaping work a path was being cut along the quarry floor. This exposed the layers of sandstone and shale originally underneath the whinstone and the tops of the fossil trees preserved in these rocks were noticed by the workmen. A careful excavation of the site was carried out, removing the rock surrounding the fossils. Initially only five of the stumps with their root systems were uncovered but work continued to reveal all the remains exposed today.

It is fortunate that those involved in the excavations recognised the importance of the site and determined to preserve it for the future. It soon became obvious that the fossils would need some protection if the Scottish weather was not quickly to destroy what had lain preserved in rock for hundreds of millions of years. The local authorities decided therefore to build a shelter over the trees. As a temporary measure the site was covered to insulate it from the effects of frost and rain before the fossil house was constructed and opened to the public on New Year's Day, 1890, just three years after the discovery. Since that date numerous improvements have been made to upgrade the original building and enhance the site.

Following their discovery, the rock surrounding the stumps was carefully removed.

WHAT TO SEE

A THE FOSSILS

The most striking features within the Grove are the fossil tree stumps. Each consists of the base of the trunk together with its spreading roots. The dimensions vary from stump to stump but the tallest stand up about 90cm from the rock floor and they reach a maximum of 1 metre across. The root system spreads out almost horizontally. Four large roots arise like buttresses from the base of the trunk and each of these divides almost immediately into two equal branches. Where preserved there is a further division so that the main root system consists of sixteen branches.

In total there are eleven of these stumps preserved in the Grove but only eight are large and easily spotted. Of the smaller examples stump four is low, only sticking up about 15cm, and is hidden by its larger neighbour (stump three), while stump eight is mostly enclosed within the rock strata along the north wall. Stump two is also small and unlike the others is not still attached to the rock floor. Its position can be determined with a fair degree of certainty using photographs taken at the time of the excavation. Stump nine was damaged during the

Second World War presumably due to bomb blast. As a result its centre section disintegrated and a concrete spacer had to be inserted.

The stumps are not circular in cross-section as they would have been in life but are ellipsoid with the long diameter of each orientated in the same direction, that is from northeast to southwest. This was attributed to deformation due to pressure on the rocks after fossilisation but more recently it has been proposed that the shape was produced by 'streamlining' of the partially decayed trunks by the flood waters that engulfed the trees. A strong water current from the southwest distorted the trees parallel to the flow and sediment deposited around and in the trunks retained the modified shape.

These waters also carried plant debris and an assortment of this flotsam was washed into the area and left stranded among the tree stumps. Fossil remains of this drifted material, ranging in size from large logs to smaller pieces of branch and root, can be seen lying on the rock surfaces. The largest, situated near the east viewing balcony, is a fallen tree trunk around 8.2 metres long.

Fallen trunk of a giant clubmoss lying on the rock floor among the stumps

One of the fossil stumps (number seven on plan) together with its major roots. This example stands about 90cm high.

B THE ROCKS

The tree stumps were preserved within layers of sandstone and shale. These rocks, which had to be cut through and partially removed to uncover the fossils, now form the banks along the edges of the excavated area. Sandstone and shale are sedimentary rocks originally deposited as flat-lying sheets of soft sand and mud which later hardened into the layers of solid rock seen at the Grove today. The soil in which the trees grew is preserved as a layer of shale at the bottom of this sequence, level with the fossil roots. The overlying layers of sandstone and shale were deposited by the water which flooded the forest and led to the death of the trees. Small wave-like undulations known as ripple marks have been preserved on some of the sandstone surfaces. These were produced by water currents which moulded the once soft sediment just as wave motion forms the familiar ripples found in the sand on the lower reaches of present-day beaches.

Around the end of the coal age some 40 million years after the death of the Fossil Grove trees there was volcanic activity in the area. The sediments and fossils were already deeply buried and hardened by this time. Rising molten rock forced its way between the layers of sandstone and shale. Here, unlike lava erupted through volcanoes, it cooled underground to produce the dolerite or whinstone also present at the Grove. The main part of the intrusion forms the wall of the quarry and lies above the fossil bed. Other smaller offshoots forced their way between the sediments at a slightly lower level and one of these now forms much of the floor of the Grove under the fossils. Another thin layer of dolerite can be seen to cut right through stump eight.

Layers of sandstone and shale along the north side of the excavated area behind stump three

Ripple marks on the surface of one of the sandstone layers

How Old?

The trees at Fossil Grove were alive and growing around 330 million years ago during a period of time known to geologists as the Carboniferous Period or, more informally, as the coal age. This lasted about 73 million years beginning 363 and ending 290 million years ago. The name derived from the fact that there are many coal seams present in the thick sequence of rock strata formed during this period.

GEOLOGICAL PERIOD	MILLIONS OF YEARS AGO
QUATERNARY	1·6
TERTIARY	65
CRETACEOUS	146
JURASSIC	208
TRIASSIC	245
PERMIAN	290
CARBONIFEROUS (COAL AGE)	330 ← AGE OF FOSSIL GROVE / 363
DEVONIAN	409
SILURIAN	439
ORDOVICIAN	510
CAMBRIAN	570
PRECAMBRIAN	4600

Giant Clubmosses and Their Relatives

The preserved remains at Fossil Grove are those of giant, extinct members of a group of primitive plants called clubmosses. These are allied to the more familiar ferns and horsetails. Giant clubmosses are also sometimes known as scale trees on account of the pattern of scale-like markings on the surface of their bark. Clubmosses first evolved about 400 million years ago and were among the earliest of land plants. Most were small herbaceous plants and the remarkable giant forms which developed and flourished during the coal age are therefore not typical.

Clubmosses still survive today. Living clubmosses, like the majority of their ancestors, are generally low-growing plants with a somewhat moss-like appearance. Although widely distributed around the world there are relatively few existing species and they are only a minor component of the present-day flora. A small number of species occur in Scotland where they are mainly restricted to

Alpine clubmoss, a living relative of Lepidodendron, *growing at Glen Feshie, Scotland. Photograph by T Norman Tait, Department of Botany, University of Glasgow*

mountain and moorland areas. These tiny plants are therefore the closest living relatives of the giant trees represented by the Fossil Grove remains and are the only remnant of this ancient group which once dominated the vegetation.

Many different kinds of giant clubmosses grew in the coal age forests. Fossil remains of the trunks and branches from these different species can be distinguished where the characteristic pattern of their bark surface is preserved. Unfortunately no trace of the bark pattern exists on the Fossil Grove stumps themselves but it is preserved on an isolated fragment of branch also present in the rocks at the site. Mainly on this evidence the remains, including the stumps, have been identified as belonging to *Lepidodendron*, probably the commonest and largest of the giant clubmosses.

Fragment of Lepidodendron *branch preserved at the Fossil Grove showing the distinctive pattern of diamond-shaped leaf scars*

R ECONSTRUCTING A
L EPIDODENDRON T REE

Giant clubmoss fossils are common in rocks of the
coal age although they are rarely as spectacular as
the Fossil Grove examples. When these large plants
died they tended, like all plants, to break up and
their fossil remains therefore are normally isolated
fragments. Pieces of the trunk, branches, roots,
leaves and cones are preserved separately. This
makes it difficult to determine, for example, which
branch belongs to which root. For this reason different parts of the same fossil plant species often have
different names.

This is true of *Lepidodendron*, the giant clubmoss preserved at Fossil Grove. Strictly the name
Lepidodendron, although applied to the tree as a
whole, relates to fossils of the trunk and branches.
Among other parts of the tree, the roots, probably
the most commonly preserved, are called *Stigmaria*
and the isolated cones *Lepidostrobus*. To build up a
picture of the complete *Lepidodendron* plant it is
necessary to piece together evidence that has been
gathered over the years from such fragmentary
remains.

What did *Lepidodendron* look like? It was cer-
tainly among the most spectacular plants of the
time, growing into a huge tree over 40 metres high.
In comparison to present-day trees *Lepidodendron*
did not attain the height of the tallest, the redwoods
of America's west coast, which can reach over 100
metres, but it would have towered over large
British trees such as the oak or beech which

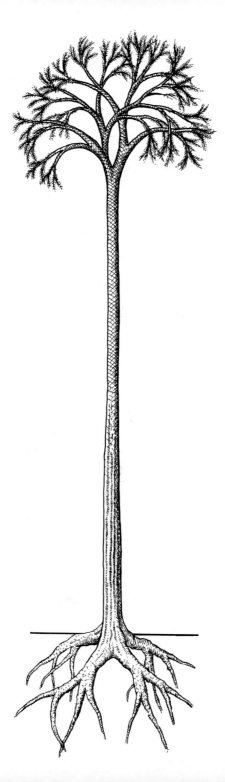

normally only reach around 30 metres in maturity. A long trunk rose straight and unbranched for much of the height of the tree before dividing repeatedly to form a dense crown of branches. At the points of division the branches always forked into two equal-sized shoots. This is distinct from present-day trees in which forking typically involves a smaller shoot branching off the main one.

The leaves which grew directly from leaf bases on the surface of the bark were retained only on the smaller branches. Here they were arranged in a spiral pattern and were closely set to form a dense covering. Although the leaves were shed from the older limbs the leaf bases remained, producing a regular pattern of diamond-shaped scars on the bark. This pattern is typical of fossilised *Lepidodendron* branches. The leaf bases too tended to be shed from much of the trunk and the surface pattern here was lost. *Lepidodendron* was shallow rooting. A small number of major roots, *Stigmaria*, spread out widely and almost horizontally to anchor the plant. The trunk divided initially into four roots at its base and each of these usually divided only twice to form the main network. Small, short rootlets grew out at right angles from these large roots giving them the appearance of a bottlebrush. Lengths of these fossilised roots can be easily distinguished from those of the branches by their surface markings which on *Stigmaria* consist of small, widely-spaced, circular scars. These mark the points where the rootlets were once attached. *Lepidodendron* bore cones which hung from the ends of small branches. The *Lepidostrobus* cones were roughly similar in appearance to pine or spruce cones but contained reproductive spores not seeds.

Internally *Lepidodendron* was also unlike present-day trees as its trunk and branches were not formed of solid wood. For strength and rigidity it relied on its tough outer bark. This enclosed an interior mainly composed of a soft pithy material with only a slender column of wood in the centre.

Lepidodendron
the bark surface
of a branch

Lepidostrobus
a giant clubmoss cone
from near
Muirkirk, Scotland

Stigmaria–
section of a giant
clubmoss root.
Note the circular
markings which
show where small
rootlets were

HOW THE FOSSILS WERE FORMED

The stumps preserved at Fossil Grove are composed entirely of sandstone. No trace of the original plant material remains. The trees have not been 'turned into stone' but are natural casts, retaining the original form of the trunk and roots. The following steps outline the process by which the living plants were converted into the fossils seen today–

1 The area of forest in which the trees were growing was flooded and sandy sediment carried by the water was deposited around the base.

2 The trees died and their upper parts broke off to float away.

3 The soft interior of the stumps rotted leaving only the outer bark.

4 Deposition of sand continued, burying the stumps. At the same time sand was also being washed in to fill the now hollow stump and roots.

5 Further layers of sediment were deposited and in the course of time the deeply buried sand both inside and outside the stump was consolidated into sandstone. The bark sandwiched between was compressed into a thin layer of coaly material.

6 Earth movements uplifted and deformed the rocks. Evidence of these movements is provided in the Grove by the dip of the rock layers. These were originally laid down as flat-lying spreads of sand and mud but must have been tilted at a later date to their present angle, sloping gently down to the northeast.

7 Once uplifted the rocks were subjected to the forces of erosion and over a long period of time the overlying layers were stripped away. The final exposure of the fossils was done by man. Quarrying of the dolerite exposed the tops of the stumps before the surrounding sandstone, which was the sand that originally engulfed the trees, was removed during the excavation. Any remaining coaly material formed by compression of the bark must have flaked away at this stage to leave the stumps as they appear today.

What remains are natural sandstone casts of the inside of the trunk and roots, formed from the sand deposited inside the hollowed-out bark. It can be seen that the internal structure of the trees was important to the way in which they have been preserved as fossils. The processes can be likened to the production of a plaster cast. The hollowed-out bark formed the mould while the sand washed into the rotten stump acted like liquid plaster hardening, albeit over a very long time, to take on the features of the enclosing mould.

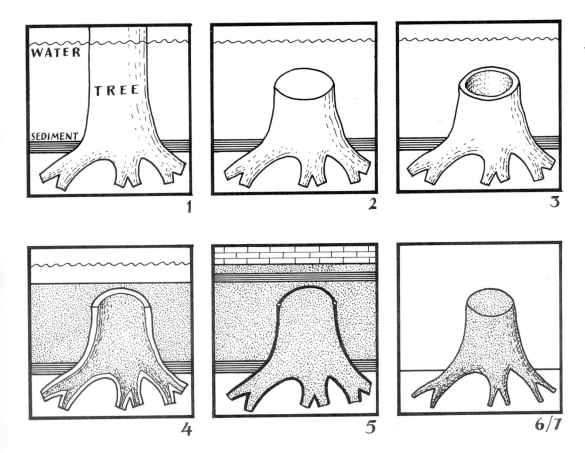

WATER

TREE

SEDIMENT

1

2

3

4

5

6/7

*Steps in the
fossilisation process
(numbers refer to text)*

19

THE FOSSIL GROVE WORLD

The Fossil Grove trees grew in an environment totally unlike that of Scotland today. The geography of this part of the earth's crust, of which Scotland's present outline and landscape are a part, is only the latest situation in a constantly changing scene. Although the changes wrought by the forces of nature take place very slowly, usually too slowly to produce noticeable results in a lifetime, their effect accumulates and over longer time scales measured in many millions of years they are capable of transforming the landscape over and over again.

Scotland is not even in the same position on the earth's surface as it was during the coal age. Internal forces within the earth power movements of the crust. The continents drift over the surface of the globe, sometimes colliding and sometimes splitting apart, so that their shape and distribution are constantly changing through time. At the time when the Fossil Grove trees were growing Scotland was situated on the equator and has gradually drifted northwards to its present position over the intervening 330 million years.

So what was Scotland like at this time? It was situated near the margin of a large continent formed of what is now North America and northern Europe. An ocean lay to the south. The environment on this continental margin was one of river flood plains and deltas forming extensive areas of flat, low-lying land liable to flooding and close to sea level. Much of the land was swampy and there would have been pools and larger bodies of open water. Being on the equator the climate was hot and humid with a high rainfall. These wetlands were swathed in dense, tropical forest of which the Fossil Grove was a tiny part. Giant clubmosses, like those preserved at the site, were common and dominant plants among the luxuriant vegetation of this huge forest.

Forests like the one to which Fossil Grove belonged were a major feature of the coal age world. They existed for many millions of years and were distributed widely, covering vast areas of lowland around the tropics of the time. The coal seams which are the remains of these forests are found today in a belt stretching from North America through Britain, Europe and Asia as far as China. Although containing different plants they can be looked on as the tropical rain forests of their day, comparable for example to the modern Amazon. They did not persist in any one area throughout the coal age. Flooding periodically destroyed the forests, as it did at the Fossil Grove, but when conditions allowed, the vegetation recolonised the area.

Giant clubmosses were common plants in the coal age forests

Coal Age Plants

A rich variety of life flourished in the forests of 330 million years ago. The vegetation was however very different to that of a present-day forest with primitive forms dominant. The flowering plants, so familiar throughout the world today, had not yet evolved; there were no flowers such as daisies or roses, no modern-type trees like oaks or elms and no grasses. Instead, growing alongside the giant clubmosses were plants such as horsetails and ferns.

Horsetails are represented today by only a few surviving species but their range is almost world-wide. Locally in Scotland they are relatively common plants occurring in wet places, woods, waste ground and even in gardens where they can be a persistent weed. Small, herbaceous horsetails very similar to living species grew during the coal age but, just like the clubmosses, giant tree-sized forms also flourished. *Calamites* was the commonest of these, growing to 20 metres. Apart from its size *Calamites* had the typical appearance of a horsetail.

It had a main stem jointed at intervals along its length, reminiscent of bamboo canes, with circles of branches growing from each of the joints. The leaves were arranged in spoke-like circles arising from the joints of small branches.

Ferns, or more accurately plants with fern-like leaves, were also a major component of the flora. Two completely different groups of plants–true ferns and seed ferns–had similar, much divided fronds and they are difficult to distinguish by fossil foliage alone. The true ferns, which reproduce by means of minute spores, usually situated on the under sides of the leaves, are still thriving today and include all living ferns. On the other hand the now extinct seed ferns were among the earliest seed-bearing plants and are considered to be more advanced. They belong to the same group, the gymnosperms, as present-day conifers. During the coal age both true ferns and seed ferns ranged in size from trees to small creeping forms.

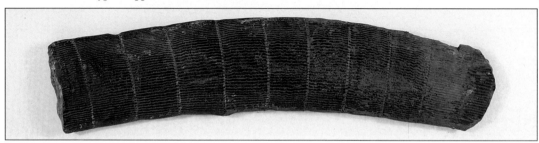

Calamites
giant horsetail stem from New Cumnock, Scotland

Asterophyllites–
a leafy shoot of a fossil horsetail,
Lesmahagow, Scotland

A present-day horsetail

Neuropteris–
foliage of
a fossil seed fern,
Carluke, Scotland

Animals of the Coal Forests

Fossil Grove itself tells us little of the animal life of the forests at this time. Apart from the trees, no other remains can be seen at the site today although it was recorded that fossil burrows, traces of the activity of worms once living in the sandy sediments, were found in some of the sandstones during the excavations.

This does not mean that the Fossil Grove forest was devoid of life; this was far from the case. Evidence of fossils from other sites where rocks of the same age are present show that the forests at this time were home to a rich variety of different animals. Freshwater mussels and fish lived in the pools, lagoons and rivers. Ancient amphibians, relatives of today's frogs and newts, also swam in these waters and walked on the land while the early ancestors of reptiles were making an appearance.

Birds and mammals had not yet evolved and even the now long extinct dinosaurs were not to appear for another 100 million years. Spiders, scorpions and many different types of insect thrived in the tropical conditions. Many grew to a huge size, including *Arthropleura*, a 2-metre long, centipede-like animal. It must have been a fearsome sight but this giant was a harmless plant eater mostly living among the leaf litter on the forest floor. A fossil specimen, found with its gut preserved, had been eating vegetable matter including fragments of giant clubmoss before it died. A track thought to belong to *Arthropleura* was found on the Isle of Arran in rocks of about the same age as those at Fossil Grove. Two parallel rows of imprints produced by its feet run 6.25 metres across the rock surface.

Model of Arthropleura. *Photograph by permission of Hunterian Museum, University of Glasgow*